45p

THE RHYMING RIVER

II

POETRY BOOKS BY JAMES REEVES

THE RHYMING RIVER
BOOK TWO

an anthology of verse chosen by
JAMES REEVES

with illustrations by
JANE PATON
and from contemporary sources

HEINEMANN EDUCATIONAL
BOOKS LTD · LONDON

Heinemann Educational Books Ltd
LONDON   MELBOURNE   TORONTO
SINGAPORE   JOHANNESBURG
HONG KONG   NAIROBI
AUCKLAND   IBADAN

First published 1959
Reprinted 1960, 1966, 1967

Published by
Heinemann Educational Books Ltd
48 Charles Street, London W.1
Printed in Great Britain by
Butler & Tanner Ltd
Frome and London

CONTENTS

I

II

ACKNOWLEDGEMENTS

THE EDITOR and publishers wish to thank the following for their permission to include copyright material in this anthology: Messrs Allan & Co. Pty Ltd, Melbourne, for 'Waltzing Matilda' by Andrew Barton Paterson; Messrs Basil Blackwell Ltd for 'The Lizard' and 'New Sights' by E. L. M. King; Messrs Boosey & Hawkes Ltd for 'O what if the Fowler my Blackbird has Taken?'; Mrs H. M. Davies and Messrs Jonathan Cape Ltd for 'A Strange Meeting', 'The Cat', and 'The Rabbit' from *The Collected Poems of W. H. Davies*; Messrs Jonathan Cape Ltd for 'A Windy Day' from *The Collected Poems of Andrew Young*; Messrs Constable & Co. Ltd for three poems by Arthur Waley; Messrs Macmillan & Co. Ltd for three poems by Thomas Hardy, and 'The Yarn of the Nancy Bell' from *The Bab Ballads* by W. S. Gilbert; Mrs W. B. Yeats and Messrs Macmillan & Co. Ltd for 'The Fiddler of Dooney' from *Collected Poems of W. B. Yeats*; the Macmillan Company, New York, for 'The Firemen's Ball' by Vachel Lindsay; the Oxford University Press for 'Diddling' from *The Blackbird and the Lilac* by James Reeves; Mrs Helen Thomas and Messrs Faber & Faber for 'A Cat' by Edward Thomas; the Literary Trustees of the late Walter de la Mare and Messrs Faber & Faber for two poems by Walter de la Mare. 'Grey' and 'Mr Tom Narrow' are taken from *The Wandering Moon* by James Reeves (Heinemann). Thanks are also due to the Trustees of the National Portrait Gallery for the illustrations on pages 6 and 46, to the Trustees of the National Maritime Museum, Greenwich, for the illustrations on pages 51 and 66, and to Mrs E. F. Rawnsley for the portrait on page 76.

Song

THE feathers of the willow
Are half of them grown yellow
    Above the swelling stream;
And ragged are the bushes,
And rusty now the rushes,
    And wild the clouded gleam.

The thistle now is older,
His stalk begins to moulder,
    His head is white as snow;
The branches all are barer,
The linnet's song is rarer,
    The robin pipeth now.

RICHARD WATSON DIXON

The Lizard

LITTLE lizard, all alone,
Basking on that sunny stone,
Which you match so cunningly,
You are very hard to see;
Still too as a stone you lie;
But I see a shining eye,
And I know that if I made
One step forward, like a shade
Quietly you would be gone,
Little spirit of the stone.

E. L. M. KING

The Sun Has Long Been Set

THE sun has long been set,
    The stars are out by twos and threes,
The little birds are piping yet
    Among the bushes and trees;
There's a cuckoo, and one or two thrushes,
And a far-off wind that rushes,
And a sound of water that gushes,
And the cuckoo's sovereign cry
Fills all the hollow of the sky.

    Who would go 'parading'
In London, 'and masquerading,'
On such a night of June
With that beautiful soft half-moon,
And all these innocent blisses?
On such a night as this is!

WILLIAM WORDSWORTH

A Windy Day

THE wind brings all dead things to life,
Branches that lash the air like whips
And dead leaves rolling in a hurry
Or peering in a rabbit's bury
Or trying to push down a tree;
Gates that fly open to the wind
And close again behind,
And fields that are a flowing sea
And make the cattle look like ships;
Straws glistening and stiff
Lying on air as on a shelf
And pond that leaps to leave itself;
And feathers too that rise and float,
Each feather changed into a bird,
And line-hung sheets that crack and strain;
Even the sun-greened coat,
That through so many winds has served,
The scarecrow struggles to put on again.

ANDREW YOUNG

3

The Eagle

HE clasps the crag with crooked hands;
Close to the sun in lonely lands,
Ring'd with the azure world, he stands.

The wrinkled sea beneath him crawls;
He watches from his mountain walls,
And like a thunderbolt he falls.

ALFRED, LORD TENNYSON

The Lark

SWIFT through the yielding air I glide,
While night's sable shades abide:
Yet in my flight (though ne'er so fast)
I tune and time the wild wind's blast:
And ere the sun be come about,
Teach the young lark his lesson out;
Who early as the day is born
Sings his shrill anthem to the rising morn:

Let never mortal lose the pains
To imitate my airy strains,
Whose pitch too high for human ears,
Was set me by the tuneful spheres.
I carol to the fairies' King,
Wake him a-mornings when I sing:
And when the sun stoops to the deep,
Rock him again and his fair Queen asleep.

ANONYMOUS

Hares at Play

THE birds are gone to bed, the cows are still,
The sheep lie panting on each old mole-hill;
And underneath the willow's grey-green bough,
Like toil a-resting, lies the fallow plough.
The timid hares throw daylight fears away
On the lane's road to dust and dance and play,
Then dabble in the grain by naught deterred
To lick the dew-fall from the barley's beard;
Then out they sturt again and round the hill
Like happy thoughts dance, squat, and loiter still,
Till milking maidens in the early morn
Jingle their yokes and sturt them in the corn;
Through well-known beaten paths each nimbling hare
Sturts quick as fear, and seeks its hidden lair.

JOHN CLARE

JOHN CLARE 1793–1864
from a painting by William Hilton

Signs of Winter

THE cat runs races with her tail. The dog
Leaps o'er the orchard hedge and knarls the grass.
The swine run round and grunt and play with straw,
Snatching out hasty mouthfuls from the stack.
Sudden upon the elm-tree tops the crow
Unceremonious visit pays and croaks,
Then swops away. From mossy barn the owl
Bobs hasty out—wheels round and, scared as soon,
As hastily retires. The ducks grow wild
And from the muddy pond fly up and wheel
A circle round the village and soon, tired,
Plunge in the pond again. The maids in haste
Snatch from the orchard hedge the mizzled clothes
And laughing hurry in to keep them dry.

JOHN CLARE

The Thrush's Nest

WITHIN a thick and spreading hawthorn bush,
That overhung a molehill large and round,
I heard from morn to morn a merry thrush
Sing hymns to sunrise, and I drank the sound
With joy; and, often an intruding guest,
I watched her secret toils from day to day—

How true she warped the moss, to form a nest,
And modelled it within with wood and clay;
And by and by, like heath-bells gilt with dew,
There lay her shining eggs, as bright as flowers,
Ink-spotted-over shells of greeny blue;
And there I witnessed in the sunny hours
A brood of nature's minstrels chirp and fly,
Glad as that sunshine and the laughing sky.

JOHN CLARE

8

The Fear of Flowers

THE nodding oxeye bends before the wind,
The woodbine quakes lest boys their flowers should find,
And prickly dogrose spite of its array
Can't dare the blossom-seeking hand away,
While thistles wear their heavy knobs of bloom
Proud as a warhorse wears its haughty plume,
And by the roadside danger's self defy;
On commons where pined[1] sheep and oxen lie
In ruddy pomp and ever thronging mood
It stands and spreads like danger in a wood,
And in the village street where meanest weeds
Can't stand untouched to fill their husks with seeds,
The haughty thistle o'er all danger towers,
In every place the very wasp of flowers.

JOHN CLARE

[1] Hungry

Song

IN the heart of the thorn is the thrush,
   On its breast is the flower of the May:
On its knees is the head of the rush,
   At its feet are the buttercups gay.

RICHARD WATSON DIXON

Old Ben

Sad is old Ben Thistlewaite,
  Now his day is done,
And all his children
  Far away are gone.

He sits beneath his jasmined porch,
  His stick beneath his knees,
His eyes fixed vacant
  On his moss-grown trees.

Grass springs in the green path,
  His flowers are lean and dry,
His thatch hangs in wisps against
  The evening sky.

He has no heart to care now,
  Though the winds will blow
Whistling in his casement,
  And the rain drip thro'.

He thinks of his old Bettie,
  How she'd shake her head and say,
'You'll live to wish my sharp old tongue
  Could scold—some day.'

But as in pale high autumn skies
  The swallows float and play,
His restless thoughts pass to and fro,
  But nowhere stay.

Soft, on the morrow, they are gone
    His garden then will be
Denser and shadier and greener,
    Greener the moss-grown tree.

WALTER DE LA MARE

The Country Lad

Who can live in heart so glad
As the merry country lad?
Who upon a fair green balk[1]
May at pleasure sit and walk,
And amid the azure skies
See the morning sun arise,
While he hears in every spring
How the birds do chirp and sing:
Or before the hounds in cry
See the hare go stealing by:
Or along the shallow brook,
Angling with a baited hook,
See the fishes leap and play
In a blessed sunny day:
Or to hear the partridge call
Till she have her covey all:
Or to see the subtle fox,
How the villain plies the box;[2]
After feeding on his prey,
How he closely sneaks away,
Through the hedge and down the furrow
Till he gets into his burrow:

---

[1] Bank.   [2] Raids the chicken run.

Then the bee to gather honey;
And the little black-haired coney,[1]
On a bank for sunny place,
With her forefeet wash her face,—
Are not these, with thousands moe
Than the courts of kings do know,
The true pleasing spirit's sights
That may breed true love's delights?

NICHOLAS BRETON

[1] Rabbit.

Pied Beauty

GLORY be to God for dappled things—
   For skies of couple-colour as a brinded cow;
     For rose-moles all in stipple upon trout that swim;
Fresh-firecoal chestnut-falls; finches' wings;
   Landscape plotted and pierced—fold, fallow, and plough;
     And áll trádes, their gear and tackle and trim.

All things counter, original, spare, strange;
   Whatever is fickle, freckled (who knows how?)
     With swift, slow; sweet, sour; adazzle, dim;
He fathers-forth whose beauty is past change: Praise Him.

GERARD MANLEY HOPKINS

A Widow Bird

A WIDOW bird sate mourning for her love
    Upon a wintry bough;
The frozen wind crept on above,
    The freezing stream below.

There was no leaf upon the forest bare,
    No flower upon the ground,
And little motion in the air
    Except the mill-wheel's sound.

                PERCY BYSSHE SHELLEY

Grey

GREY is the sky, and grey the woodman's cot
With grey smoke tumbling from the chimney-pot.
The flagstones are grey that lead to the door;
Grey is the hearth, and grey the worn old floor.

The old man by the fire nods in his chair;
Grey are his clothes and silvery grey his hair.
Grey are the shadows around him creeping,
And grey the mouse from the corner peeping.

                JAMES REEVES

Epitaphs

ROBERT DALUSSE

As flowers in the field, thus passeth life,
Naked, then clothed, feeble in the end,
It sheweth by Robert Dalusse, and Alison his wife,
Christ them save from the power of the fiend.

MARTIN ELGINBRODDE

Here lie I, Martin Elginbrodde:
Ha'e mercy o' my soul, Lord God,
As I wad do, were I Lord God
And ye were Martin Elginbrodde.

MARTHA SNELL

Poor Martha Snell has gone away,
Her would, if she could, but she couldn't stay,
She had two sore legs and a baddish cough,
But it were her legs that carried her off.

ANONYMOUS

The Poplar Field

THE poplars are felled, farewell to the shade
And the whispering sound of the cool colonnade,
The winds play no longer, and sing in the leaves,
Nor Ouse in his bosom their image receives.

Twelve years have elapsed since I first took a view
Of my favourite field and the bank where they grew,
And now in the grass behold they are laid,
And the tree is my seat that once lent me a shade.

The blackbird has fled to another retreat
Where the hazels afford him a screen from the heat,
And the scene where his melody charmed me before
Resounds with his sweet-flowing ditty no more.

My fugitive years are all hasting away,
And I must ere long lie as lowly as they,
With a turf on my breast, and a stone on my head,
Ere another such grove shall arise in its stead.

'Tis a sight to engage me, if anything can,
To muse on the perishing pleasures of man;
Though his life be a dream, his enjoyments, I see,
Have a being less durable even than he.

WILLIAM COWPER

Cavalry Crossing a Ford

A LINE in long array where they wind betwixt green islands,
They take a serpentine course, their arms flash in the sun—hark
  to the musical clank,
Behold the silvery river, in it the splashing horses loitering stop
  to drink,
Behold the brown-faced men, each group, each person a picture,
  the negligent rest on the saddles,
Some emerge on the opposite bank, others are just entering the
  ford—while,

Scarlet and blue and snowy white,
The guidon flags flutter gayly in the wind.
To cheer one on the tedious way,
To fetch one if one goes astray,
To lift one if one totters down,
To strengthen whilst one stands.

WALT WHITMAN

The Dismantled Ship

IN some unused lagoon, some nameless bay,
On sluggish, lonesome waters, anchor'd near the shore,
An old, dismasted, gray and batter'd ship, disabled, done,
After free voyages to all the seas of earth, haul'd up at last and
    hawser'd tight,
Lies rusting, mouldering.

WALT WHITMAN

II

Boating in Autumn

AWAY and away I sail in my light boat;
My heart leaps with a great gust of joy.
Through the leafless branches I see the temple in the wood;
Over the dwindling stream the stone bridge towers.
Down the grassy lanes sheep and oxen pass;
In the misty village cranes and magpies cry.

Back in my home I drink a cup of wine
And need not fear the greed of the evening wind.

ARTHUR WALEY

The Caged Goldfinch

WITHIN a churchyard, on a recent grave,
  I saw a little cage
That jailed a goldfinch. All was silence save
  Its hops from stage to stage.

There was inquiry in its wistful eye,
  And once it tried to sing;
Of him or her who placed it there, and why,
  No one knew anything.

THOMAS HARDY

Weathers

THIS is the weather the cuckoo likes,
  And so do I;
When showers betumble the chestnut spikes,
  And nestlings fly:
And the little brown nightingale bills his best,
And they sit outside at 'The Travellers' Rest,'
And maids come forth sprig-muslin drest,
And citizens dream of the south and west,
  And so do I.

This is the weather the shepherd shuns,
  And so do I;
When beeches drip in browns and duns,
  And thresh, and ply;
The hill-hid tides throb, throe on throe,
And meadow rivulets overflow,
And drops on gate-bars hang in a row,
And rooks in families homeward go,
  And so do I.

THOMAS HARDY

Lo-Yang

A BEAUTIFUL place is the town of Lo-yang;
The big streets are full of spring light.
The lads go driving out with harps in their hands:
The mulberry girls go out to the fields with their baskets.
Golden whips glint at the horses' flanks,
Gauze sleeves brush the green boughs.
Racing dawn, the carriages come home,—
And the girls with their high baskets full of fruit.

ARTHUR WALEY

The Splendour Falls on Castle Walls

THE splendour falls on castle walls
  And snowy summits old in story:
The long light shakes across the lakes,
  And the wild cataract leaps in glory.
Blow, bugle, blow, set the wild echoes flying,
Blow, bugle; answer, echoes, dying, dying, dying.

O hark, O hear! how thin and clear,
  And thinner, clearer, farther going!
O sweet and far from cliff and scar
  The horns of Elfland faintly blowing!
Blow, let us hear the purple glens replying:
Blow, bugle; answer, echoes, dying, dying, dying.

O love, they die in yon rich sky,
  They faint on hill or field or river:
Our echoes roll from soul to soul,
  And grow for ever and for ever.
Blow, bugle, blow, set the wild echoes flying,
And answer, echoes, answer, dying, dying, dying.

ALFRED, LORD TENNYSON

At Fifteen I went with the Army

At fifteen I went with the army,
At fourscore I came home.
On the way I met a man from the village,
I asked him who there was at home.
'That over there is your house,
All covered over with trees and bushes.'
Rabbits had run in at the dog-hole,
Pheasants flew down from the beams of the roof.
In the courtyard was growing some wild grain;
And by the well, some wild mallows.
I'll boil the grain and make porridge,
I'll pluck the mallows and make soup.
Soup and porridge are both cooked,
But there is no one to eat them with.
I went out and looked towards the east,
While tears fell and wetted my clothes.

ARTHUR WALEY

The Pedlar of Spells

An old man selling charms in a cranny of the town wall.
He writes out spells to bless the silkworm and spells to protect
    the corn.
With the money he gets each day he only buys wine.
But he does not worry when his legs get wobbly,
For he has a boy to lean on.

ARTHUR WALEY

Full Moon

ONE night as Dick lay fast asleep,
  Into his drowsy eyes
A great still light began to creep
  From out the silent skies.
It was the lovely moon's, for when
  He raised his dreamy head,
Her surge of silver filled the pane
  And streamed across his bed.
So, for awhile, each gazed at each—
  Dick and the solemn moon—
Till, climbing slowly on her way,
  She vanished, and was gone.

WALTER DE LA MARE

I Will Give My Love an Apple

I WILL give my love an apple without e'er a core,
I will give my love a house without e'er a door,
I will give my love a palace wherein she may be,
And she may unlock it without any key.

My head is the apple without e'er a core,
My mind is the house without e'er a door,
My heart is the palace wherein she may be,
And she may unlock it without any key.

TRADITIONAL

Evening: Ponte al Mare, Pisa

THE sun is set; the swallows are asleep;
   The bats are flitting fast in the gray air;
The slow soft toads out of damp corners creep,
   And evening's breath, wandering here and there
Over the quivering surface of the stream,
Wakes not one ripple from its summer dream.

There is no dew on the dry grass to-night,
   Nor damp within the shadow of the trees;
The wind is intermitting, dry, and light;
   And in the inconstant motion of the breeze
The dust and straws are driven up and down,
And whirled about the pavement of the town.

Within the surface of the fleeting river
   The wrinkled image of the city lay,
Immovably unquiet, and forever
   It trembles, but it never fades away——[1]

The chasm in which the sun has sunk is shut
   By darkest barriers of cinereous cloud,
Like mountain over mountain huddled—but
   Growing and moving upwards in a crowd,
And over it a space of watery blue,
Which the keen evening star is shining through.

PERCY BYSSHE SHELLEY

[1] This verse was left unfinished.

To his Maid Prew

THESE summer birds did with thy master stay
The times of warmth; but then they flew away:
Leaving their poet, being now grown old,
Exposed to all the coming winter's cold.
But thou, kind Prew, didst with my fates abide,
As well the winter's, as the summer's tide:
For which thy love, live with thy master here,
Not two, but all the seasons of the year.

ROBERT HERRICK

Country Letter

DEAR brother robin this comes from us all
With our kind love and could Gip write and all
Though but a dog he'd have his love to spare
For still he knows and by your corner chair
The moment he comes in he lyes him down
and seems to fancy you are in the town.
This leaves us well in health thank God for that
For old acquaintance Sue has kept your hat
Which mother brushes ere she lays it bye
and every sunday goes upstairs to cry
Jane still is yours till you come back agen
and neer so much as dances with the men
and ned the woodman every week comes in
and asks about you kindly as our kin
and he with this and goody Thompson sends
Remembrances with those of all our friends

26

Father with us sends love untill he hears
and mother she has nothing but her tears
Yet wishes you like us in health the same
and longs to see a letter with your name
So loving brother don't forget to write
Old Gip lies on the hearth stone every night
Mother can't bear to turn him out of doors
and never noises now of dirty floors
Father will laugh but lets her have her way
and Gip for kindness get a double pay
So Robin write and let us quickly see
You don't forget old friends no more than we
Nor let my mother have so much to blame
To go three journeys ere your letter came.

JOHN CLARE

New Sights

I LIKE to see a thing I know
Has not been seen before,
That's why I cut my apple through
To look into the core.

It's nice to think though many an eye
Has seen the ruddy skin,
Mine is the very first to spy
The five brown pips within.

E. L. M. KING

A Cat

SHE had a name among the children;
But no one loved though someone owned
Her, locked her out of doors at bedtime
And had her kittens duly drowned.

In Spring, nevertheless, this cat
Ate blackbirds, thrushes, nightingales,
And birds of bright voice and plume and flight,
As well as scraps from neighbours' pails.

I loathed and hated her for this;
One speckle on a thrush's breast
Was worth a million such; and yet
She lived long, till God gave her rest.

EDWARD THOMAS

28

The Cat

WITHIN that porch, across the way,
I see two naked eyes this night;
Two eyes that neither shut nor blink,
Searching my face with a green light.

But cats to me are strange, so strange—
I cannot sleep if one is near;
And though I'm sure I see those eyes,
I'm not so sure a body's there!

W. H. DAVIES

The Rabbit

NOT even when the early birds
Danced on my roof with showery feet
Such music as will come from rain—
Not even then could I forget
The rabbit in his hours of pain;
Where, lying in an iron trap,
He cries all through the deafened night—
Until his smiling murderer comes,
To kill him in the morning light.

W. H. DAVIES

Who would True Valour see

(from *The Pilgrim's Progress*)

WHO would true valour see,
  Let him come hither;
One here will constant be,
  Come wind, come weather.
There's no discouragement
Shall make him once relent
His first avow'd intent
  To be a pilgrim.

Whoso beset him round
  With dismal stories,
Do but themselves confound,
  His strength the more is.
No lion can him fright,
He'll with a giant fight,
But he will have a right
  To be a pilgrim.

Hobgoblin nor foul fiend
  Can daunt his spirit;
He knows he at the end
  Shall life inherit.
Then fancies flee away!
He'll fear not what men say;
He'll labour night and day
  To be a pilgrim.

JOHN BUNYAN

A Man of Words

A MAN of words and not of deeds
Is like a garden full of weeds;
And when the weeds begin to grow
It's like a garden full of snow;
And when the snow begins to fall,
It's like a bird upon the wall;
And when the bird away does fly,
It's like an eagle in the sky;
And when the sky begins to roar,
It's like a lion at the door;
And when the door begins to crack,
It's like a stick across your back;
And when your back begins to smart,
It's like a penknife in your heart;
And when your heart begins to bleed,
You're dead, and dead, and dead indeed.

A Strange Meeting

THE moon is full, and so am I;
The night is late, the ale was good;
And I must go two miles and more
Along a country road.

Now what is this that's drawing near?
It seems a man, and tall;
But where the face should show its white
I see no white at all.

Where is his face: or do I see
The back part of his head,
And, with his face turned round about,
He walks this way? I said.

He's close at hand, but where's the face?
What devil is this I see?
I'm glad my body's warm with ale,
There's trouble here for me.

I clutch my staff, I make a halt,
'His blood or mine,' said I.
'Good-night,' the black man said to me,
As he went passing by.

W. H. DAVIES

The Fiddler of Dooney

WHEN I play on my fiddle in Dooney,
Folk dance like a wave of the sea;
My cousin is priest in Kilvarnet,
My brother in Mocharabuiee.[1]

I passed my brother and cousin:
They read in their books of prayer;
I read in my book of songs
I bought at the Sligo fair.

When we come at the end of time
To Peter sitting in state,
He will smile on the three old spirits,
But call me first through the gate;

For the good are always the merry,
Save by an evil chance,
And the merry love the fiddle,
And the merry love to dance:

And when the folk there spy me,
They will all come up to me,
With 'Here is the fiddler of Dooney!'
And dance like a wave of the sea.

W. B. YEATS

Pronounced as if spelt 'Mockrabwee'.

The Falcon

LULLY, lulley! lully, lulley!
The falcon hath borne my make[1] away!

He bare him up, he bare him down,
He bare him into an orchard brown.

In the orchard there was a hall,
That was hanged with purple and pall.

And in that hall there was a bed,
It was hanged with gold so red.

And in that bed there li'th a knight
His woundes bleeding day and night.

At that bed's foot there li'th a hound,
Licking the blood as it runs down.

By that bed-side there kneeleth a may,[2]
And she weepeth both night and day.

And at that bed's head standeth a stone,
Corpus Christi written thereon.

Lully, lulley! lully, lulley!
The falcon hath borne my make away!

[1] Sweetheart.   [2] Maid.

The Harper

ON the green banks of Shannon, when Sheelah was nigh,
No blithe Irish lad was so happy as I;
No harp like my own could so cheerily play,
And wherever I went was my poor dog Tray.

When at last I was forced from my Sheelah to part,
She said (while the sorrow was big at her heart),
'Oh! remember your Sheelah when far, far away;
And be kind, my dear Pat, to our poor dog Tray.'

Poor dog! he was faithful and kind, to be sure,
And he constantly loved me, although I was poor;
When the sour-looking folk sent me heartless away,
I had always a friend in my poor dog Tray.

When the road was so dark, and the night was so cold,
And Pat and his dog were grown weary and old,
How snugly we slept in my old coat of gray,
And he licked me for kindness—my poor dog Tray.

Though my wallet was scant I remembered his case,
Nor refused my last crust to his pitiful face;
But he died at my feet on a cold winter day,
And I played a sad lament for my poor dog Tray.

Where now shall I go, forsaken and blind?
Can I find one to guide me so faithful and kind?
To my sweet native village, so far, far away,
I can never more return with my poor dog Tray.

THOMAS CAMPBELL

The Echoing Green

THE Sun does arise
And make happy the skies;
The merry bells ring
To welcome the Spring;
The skylark and thrush,
The birds of the bush,
Sing louder around
To the bells' cheerful sound;
While our sports shall be seen
On the echoing Green.

Old John, with white hair,
Does laugh away care,
Sitting under the oak,
Among the old folk.
They laugh at our play,
And soon they all say,
'Such, such were the joys
When we all—girls and boys—
In our youth-time were seen
On the echoing Green.'

Till the little ones, weary,
No more can be merry;
The sun does descend,
And our sports have an end.
Round the laps of their mothers
Many sisters and brothers,
Like birds in their nest,
Are ready for rest,
And sport no more seen
On the darkening Green.

WILLIAM BLAKE

Ode

(*Written in the beginning of the year 1746*)

How sleep the brave, who sink to rest
By all their country's wishes blessed!
When spring, with dewy fingers cold,
Returns to deck their hallowed mould,
She there shall dress a sweeter sod
Than fancy's feet have ever trod.

By fairy hands their knell is rung,
By forms unseen their dirge is sung;
There Honour comes, a pilgrim grey,
To bless the turf that wraps their clay,
And Freedom shall awhile repair,
To dwell a weeping hermit there!

WILLIAM COLLINS

To Meadows

Ye have been fresh and green,
    Ye have been fill'd with flowers:
And ye the walks have been
    Where maids have spent their hours.

You have beheld, how they
    With wicker arks did come
To kiss, and bear away
    The richer cowslips home.

38

Y'ave heard them sweetly sing,
 And seen them in a round:
Each virgin, like a Spring,
 With honey-suckles crown'd.

But now, we see none here,
 Whose silvery feet did tread,
And with dishevell'd hair
 Adorn'd this smoother mead.

Like unthrifts, having spent
 Your stock, and needy grown,
Y'are left here to lament
 Your poor estates, alone.

ROBERT HERRICK

III

Flowers in the Valley

O THERE was a woman, and she was a widow,
Fair are the flowers in the valley.
With a daughter as fair as a fresh sunny meadow,
The Red, the Green, and the Yellow,
The Harp, the Lute, the Pipe, the Flute, the Cymbal,
Sweet goes the treble Violin
The maid so rare and the flowers so fair
Together they grew in the valley.

There came a Knight all clothed in red,
Fair are the flowers in the valley.
'I would thou wert my bride,' he said,
The Red, the Green, and the Yellow.
The Harp, the Lute, the Pipe, the Flute, the Cymbal,
Sweet goes the treble Violin.
'I would,' she sighed, 'ne'er wins a bride!'
Fair are the flowers in the valley.

There came a Knight all clothed in green,
Fair are the flowers in the valley.
'This maid so sweet might be my queen,'
The Red, the Green, and the Yellow.
The Harp, the Lute, the Pipe, the Flute, the Cymbal,
Sweet goes the treble Violin.
'Might be,' sighed she, 'will ne'er win me!'
Fair are the flowers in the valley.

There came a Knight, in yellow was he,
Fair are the flowers in the valley.
'My bride, my queen, thou must with me!'
The Red, the Green, and the Yellow.
The Harp, the Lute, the Pipe, the Flute, the Cymbal,
Sweet goes the treble Violin.
With blushes red, 'I come,' she said;
'Farewell to the flowers in the valley.'

O what if the Fowler my Blackbird has Taken?

O WHAT if the fowler my blackbird has taken?
　　The roses of dawn blossom over the sea;
Awaken, my blackbird, awaken, awaken,
　　And sing to me out of my red fuchsia tree!

O what if the fowler my blackbird has taken?
    The sun lifts his head from the lap of the sea—
Awaken, my blackbird, awaken, awaken,
    And sing to me out of my red fuchsia tree!

O what if the fowler my blackbird has taken?
    The mountain grows white with the birds of the sea;
But down in my garden forsaken, forsaken,
    I'll weep all the day by my red fuchsia tree!

CHARLES DALMON

The Raggle Taggle Gypsies

THREE gypsies stood at the Castle gate,
They sang so high, they sang so low,
The lady sate in her chamber late,
Her heart it melted away as snow.

They sang so sweet, they sang so shrill,
That fast her tears began to flow.
And she laid down her silken gown,
Her golden rings and all her show.

She plucked off her high-heeled shoes,
A-made of Spanish leather, O!
She would in the street, with her bare, bare feet,
All out in the wind and weather O!

It was late last night, when my lord came home,
Enquiring for his a-lady, O!
The servants said on every hand,
'She's gone with the raggle taggle gypsies, O!'

'O saddle to me my milk-white steed.
Go and fetch me my pony, O!
That I may ride and seek my bride,
Who is gone with the raggle taggle gypsies, O!'

O he rode high and he rode low,
He rode through woods and copses too.
Until he came to an open field,
And there he espied his a-lady, O!

'What makes you leave your house and land?
What makes you leave your money, O?
What makes you leave your new-wedded lord,
To go with the raggle taggle gypsies, O?'

'What care I for my house and my land?
What care I for my money, O?
What care I for my new-wedded lord?
I'm off with the raggle taggle gypsies, O!'

'Last night you slept on a goose-feather bed,
With the sheet turned down so bravely, O!
And tonight you'll sleep in a cold open field,
Along with the raggle taggle gypsies, O!'

'What care I for a goose-feather bed,
With the sheet turned down so bravely, O?
For tonight I shall sleep in a cold open field,
Along with the raggle taggle gypsies, O!'

We be the King's Men

We be the King's men, hale and hearty,
Marching to meet one Buonaparty;
If he won't sail, lest the wind should blow,
We shall have marched for nothing, O!
    Right fol-lol!

We be the King's men, hale and hearty,
Marching to meet one Buonaparty;
If he be sea-sick, says 'No, no!'
We shall have marched for nothing, O!
    Right fol-lol!

We be the King's men, hale and hearty,
Marching to meet one Buonaparty;
Never mind, mates; we'll be merry, though
We may have marched for nothing, O!
    Right fol-lol!

THOMAS HARDY

ROBERT BURNS 1759–1796
from a painting by Alexander Nasmyth

A Highland Lad

A HIGHLAND lad my love was born,
The Lowland laws he held in scorn,
But he still was faithful to his clan,
My gallant braw John Highlandman.

   Sing hey! my braw John Highlandman,
   Sing ho! my braw John Highlandman,
   There's not a lad in all the land,
   Was match for my John Highlandman.

With his philabeg[1] and his tartan plaid,
And good claymore down by his side,
The ladies' hearts he did trepan,[2]
My gallant braw John Highlandman.

We've ranged a' from Tweed to Spey,
And liv'd like lords and ladies gay;
For a lowlander he feared none,
My gallant braw John Highlandman.

They banished him beyond the sea,
But ere the bud was on the tree,
A down my cheeks the pearls ran,
Embracing my John Highlandman.

But, O, they catch'd him at the last,
And bound him in a dungeon fast;
My curse upon them ev'ry one,
They've hanged my braw John Highlandman.

ROBERT BURNS

[1] Kilt.   [2] Deceive.

Hares on the Mountains

IF all these young men were as hares on the mountains,
Then all these pretty maidens will get guns, go a-hunting.
With ri fol de dee, cal al de day, ri fol i dee.

If all these young men were as rushes a-growing,
Then all these pretty maidens will get scythes, go a-mowing.
With ri fol de dee, cal al de day, ri fol i dee.

If all these young men were as ducks in the water,
Then all these pretty maidens will soon follow after.
With ri fol de dee, cal al de day, ri fol i dee.

But the young men are given to frisking and fooling.
I'll let them alone and attend to my schooling.
With ri fol de dee, cal al de day, ri fol i dee.

TRADITIONAL

The Battle of Jericho

JOSHUA fit[1] de battle ob Jericho,
   Jericho, Jericho,
Joshua fit de battle ob Jericho,
   An' de walls come tumblin' down.

You may talk about yo' king ob Gideon,
You may talk about yo' man ob Saul,
Dere's none like good ole Joshua,
At de battle ob Jericho.

Up to de walls ob Jericho
He marched with spear in han',

[1] Fought.

48

'Go blow dem ram horns,' Joshua cried,
'Kase[1] de battle am in my han'.'

Den de lam'ram sheep horns begin to blow,
Trumpets begin to soun',
Joshua commanded de chillun to shout
An' de walls come tumblin' down.
                              (Dat mornin'.)

Joshua fit de battle ob Jericho,
   Jericho, Jericho,
Joshua fit de battle ob Jericho,
   An' de walls come tumblin' down.

NEGRO SPIRITUAL

Go Down, Moses

Go down, Moses,
  'Way down in Egypt land,
Tell ole Pharaoh
  To let my people go.

When Israel was in Egypt's land:
  Let my people go!
Oppressed so hard they could not stand,
  Let my people go!

Go down, Moses. . . .

  'Thus spake the Lord,' bold Moses said;
    'Let my people go!
  If not, I'll smite your first-born dead.'
    Let my people go!

Go down, Moses. . . .

NEGRO SPIRITUAL

[1] Because.

49

The Night of Trafalgár

IN the wild October night-time, when the wind raved round the
    land,
And the Back-sea[1] met the Front-sea, and our doors were blocked
    with sand,
And we heard the drub of Dead-man's Bay, where bones of
    thousands are,
We knew not what the day had done for us at Trafalgár.
       (*All*)   Had done,
            Had done,
       For us at Trafalgár!

'Pull hard, and make the Nothe, or down we go!' one says,
    says he.
We pulled; and bedtime brought the storm; but snug at home
    slept we.
Yet all the while our gallants after fighting through the day,
Were beating up and down the dark, sou'west of Cadiz Bay.
       The dark,
       The dark,
    Sou'west of Cadiz Bay!

The victors and the vanquished then the storm it tossed and tore,
As hard they strove, those worn-out men, upon that surly shore;
Dead Nelson and his half-dead crew, his foes from near and far,
Were rolled together on the deep that night at Trafalgár!
       The deep,
       The deep,
    That night at Trafalgár!

THOMAS HARDY

[1] In those days the hind-part of the harbour adjoining this scene was so named,
and at high tides the waves washed across the isthmus at a point called 'The
Narrows' (*Hardy's Note*).

THE VICTORY

from an oil painting attributed to Monamy Swaine, about 1790

A Yankee Ship

A YANKEE ship came down the river,
  Blow, boys, blow.
Her masts and yards they shine like silver.
  Blow, my bully boys, blow.

And how d'ye know she's a Yankee packet?
  Blow, boys, blow,
The Stars and Stripes they fly above her.
  Blow, my bully boys, blow.

And who d'ye think was skipper of her?
  Blow, boys, blow.
And who d'ye think was skipper of her?
  Blow, my bully boys, blow.

'Twas Dandy Jim, the one-eyed nigger;
  Blow, boys, blow.
'Twas Dandy Jim, with his bully figure.
  Blow, my bully boys, blow.

And what d'ye think they had for dinner?
  Blow, boys, blow.
Why bullock's lights and donkey's liver.
  Blow, my bully boys, blow.

And what d'ye think they had for supper?
  Blow, boys, blow.
Why weevilled bread and Yankee leather.
  Blow, my bully boys, blow.

Then blow my boys and blow together.
  Blow, boys, blow.
And blow my boys for better weather.
  Blow, my bully boys, blow.

TRADITIONAL

Santy Anna

OH Santy Anna won the day.
  Way ah, me Santy Anna.
Oh Santy Anna won the day.
  All on the plains of Mexico.

He beat the Prooshans fairly.
  Way ah, me Santy Anna.
And whacked the British nearly.
  All on the plains of Mexico.

He was a rorty gineral;
  Way ah, me Santy Anna.
A rorty snorty gineral.
  All on the plains of Mexico.

They took him out and shot him.
  Way ah, me Santy Anna.
Oh when shall we forget him.
  All on the plains of Mexico.

Oh Santy Anna won the day
  Way ah, me Santy Anna.
And Gin'ral Taylor run away.
  All on the plains of Mexico.

TRADITIONAL

Stormalong

OLD Stormy he is dead and gone,
To my way, Stormalong!
Old Stormy he is dead and gone,
Aye, aye, aye, Mister Stormalong.

Old Stormy's dead, that good old man,
To my way, Stormalong!
Old Stormy's dead, that good old man,
Aye, aye, aye, Mister Stormalong.

I carried him away to Mobile Bay,
To my way, Stormalong!
I carried him away to Mobile Bay,
Aye, aye, aye, Mister Stormalong.

I dug his grave with a silver spade,
To my way, Stormalong!
I dug his grave with a silver spade,
Aye, aye, aye, Mister Stormalong.

I lowered him down with a golden chain,
To my way, Stormalong!
I lowered him down with a golden chain,
Aye, aye, aye, Mister Stormalong.

I dug his grave full wide and deep,
  To my way, Stormalong!
And there Old Stormy lies asleep,
  Aye, aye, aye, Mister Stormalong.

I wish I was Old Stormy's son,
  To my way, Stormalong!
I'd build a ship a thousand ton,
  Aye, aye, aye, Mister Stormalong.

Old Stormy he is dead and gone,
  To my way, Stormalong!
Old Stormy he is dead and gone,
  Aye, aye, aye, Mister Stormalong.

TRADITIONAL

Haul Away Joe

WAY haul away! we'll haul away the bowline,
Way haul away! we'll haul away Joe.
Way haul away! The packet is a-rollin',
Way haul away! we'll haul away Joe.

Way haul away! we'll haul away together,
Way haul away! we'll haul away Joe.
Way haul away! we'll haul for better weather,
Way haul away! we'll haul away Joe.

Once I had a nigger girl, and she was fat and lazy.
Way haul away! we'll haul away Joe.
Then I had a Spanish girl, she nearly drove me crazy.
Way haul away! we'll haul away Joe.

Geordie Charlton had a pig, and it was double-jointed.
Way haul away! we'll haul away Joe.
He took it to the blacksmith's shop to get its trotters pointed.
Way haul away! we'll haul away Joe.

King Louis was the king of France before the Revolution.
  Way haul away! we'll haul away Joe.
King Louis got his head cut off, and spoiled his Constitution.
  Way haul away! we'll haul away Joe.

Oh when I was a little boy and so my mother told me.
  Way haul away! we'll haul away Joe.
That if I didn't kiss the girls my lips would go all mouldy.
  Way haul away! we'll haul away Joe.

Oh once I had a scolding wife, she wasn't very civil.
  Way haul away! we'll haul away Joe.
I clapped a plaster on her mouth and sent her to the devil.
  Way haul away! we'll haul away Joe.

TRADITIONAL

Lowlands

I DREAMED a dream the other night;
  Lowlands, away, my love!
My love she came dressed all in white.
  Lowlands away!

She came to me at my bedside;
  Lowlands, away, my love!
All dressed in white like some fair bride.
  Lowlands, away!

No sound she made, no word she said;
  Lowlands, away, my love!
And then I knew my love was dead.
  Lowlands, away!

TRADITIONAL

Waltzing Matilda

ONCE a jolly swagman[1] camped by a billabong[2]
  Under the shade of a coolibah tree,
And he sang as he watched and waited till his billy boiled,
  'You'll come a-waltzing Matilda[3] with me!'
Waltzing Matilda, waltzing Matilda,
  You'll come a-waltzing Matilda with me:
And he sang as he watched and waited till his billy boiled,
  'You'll come a-waltzing Matilda with me!'

Down came a jumbuck to drink at the billabong,
  Up jumped the swagman and grabbed him with glee,
And he sang as he stowed that jumbuck in his tucker bag,
  'You'll come a-waltzing Matilda with me!'
Waltzing Matilda, waltzing Matilda,
  You'll come a-waltzing Matilda with me:
And he sang as he stowed that jumbuck in his tucker bag,
  'You'll come a-waltzing Matilda with me!'

Up rode the squatter mounted on his thoroughbred,
  Up rode the troopers, one, two, three.
'Where's that jolly jumbuck you've got in your tucker-bag?
  You'll come a-waltzing Matilda with me!'
Waltzing Matilda, waltzing Matilda,
  You'll come a-waltzing Matilda with me:
Where's that jolly jumbuck you've got in your tucker-bag?
  You'll come a-waltzing Matilda with me!'

---

[1] Tramp.   [2] Water-hole.
[3] *Waltzing Matilda:* tramp from place to place carrying swag, i.e. bundle
containing what could be stolen or begged.

Up jumped the swagman and sprang into the billabong,
  'You'll never take me alive!' said he.
And his ghost may be heard as you pass by that billabong,
  'You'll never take me alive!' said he.
Waltzing Matilda, waltzing Matilda,
  You'll come a-waltzing Matilda with me,
And his ghost may be heard as you pass by that billabong,
  'You'll come a-waltzing Matilda with me!'

ANDREW BARTON PATERSON

The Island

DADDY Neptune one day to Freedom did say,
  'If ever I lived upon dry land,
The spot I should hit on would be little Britain.'
  Says Freedom, 'Why, that's my own island.'
      Oh! what a snug little Island,
      A right little, tight little Island;
    All the globe round, none can be found
      So happy as this little Island.

Julius Caesar the Roman, who yielded to no man,
  Came by water, he couldn't come *by* land!
And Dane, Pict, and Saxon their homes turned their backs on,
  And all for the sake of our Island.
      Oh! what a snug little Island,
      They'd all have a touch at the Island,
    Some were shot dead—some of them fled,
      And some stayed to live on the Island.

Then a very great war-man called Billy the Norman,
    Cried, 'Hang it! I never liked my land;
It would be much more handy to leave this Normandy,
    And live on yon beautiful Island.'
        Says he, ' 'Tis a snug little Island,
        Shan't us go visit the Island?'
      Hop, skip and jump—there he was plump,
      And he kicked up a dust in the Island.

But party deceit helped the Normans to beat,
    Of traitors they managed to buy land;
By Dane, Saxon or Pict we ne'er had been licked,
    Had they stuck to the King of their Island.
      Poor Harold, the king of the Island,
      He lost both his life and his Island;
     That's very true—what could he do?
     Like a Briton he died for his Island.

Then the Spanish Armada set out to invade-a,
    Quite sure if they ever came nigh land
They couldn't do less than tuck up Queen Bess,
    And take their full swing in the Island.
      Oh! the poor Queen and the Island,
      The drones came to plunder the Island,
     But snug in her hive, the Queen was alive,
     And buzz was the word in the Island.

These proud puffed-up cakes thought to make ducks and drakes
    Of our wealth; but they scarcely could spy land,
Ere our Drake had the luck to make their pride duck
    And stoop to the lads of the Island.

The good wooden walls of the Island;
Huzza! for the lads of the Island;
Devil or Don, let them come on,
But how'd they come off at the Island!

I don't wonder much that the French and the Dutch
Have since been oft tempted to try land,
And I wonder much less they have met no success,
For why should we give up our Island?
Oh! 'tis a wonderful Island,
All of 'em long for the Island;
Hold a bit there, let 'em take fire and air,
But we'll have the sea and the Island.

Then since Freedom and Neptune have hitherto kept tune
In each saying, 'This shall be my land';
Should the 'Army of England',[1] or all it could bring, land,
We'd show 'em some play for the Island.
We'd fight for our right to the Island,
We'd give them enough of the Island;
Invaders should just—bite at the dust,
But not a bit more of the Island.

CHARLES DIBDIN

[1] Napoleon's army of invasion.

IV

Sir John Barleycorn

THERE came three men from out the West
Their victory to try;
And they have ta'en a solemn oath,
Poor Barleycorn should die.

They took a plough and ploughed him in,
Clods harrowed on his head;
And then they took a solemn oath
John Barleycorn was dead.

There he lay sleeping in the ground
Till rain did on him fall;
Then Barleycorn sprung up his head,
And so amazed them all.

There he remained till Midsummer
And look'd both pale and wan;
Then Barleycorn he got a beard
And so became a man.

Then they sent men with scythes so sharp
To cut him off at knee;
And then poor Johnny Barleycorn
They served most barbarouslie.

Then they sent men with pitchforks strong
To pierce him through the heart;
And like a doleful Tragedy
They bound him in a cart.

And then they brought him to a barn
A prisoner to endure;
And so they fetched him out again,
And laid him on the floor.

Then they set men with holly clubs,
To beat the flesh from th' bones;
But the miller served him worse than that
He ground him 'twixt two stones.

O! Barleycorn is the choicest grain
That e'er was sown on land
It will do more than any grain,
By the turning of your hand.

It will make a boy into a man,
A man into an ass;
To silver it will change your gold,
Your silver into brass.

It will make the huntsman hunt the fox,
That never wound a horn;
It will bring the tinker to the stocks
That people may him scorn.

O! Barleycorn is th' choicest grain,
That e'er was sown on land.
And it will cause a man to drink
Till he neither can go nor stand.

TRADITIONAL

The Battle of Creçy

RIGHT gory and messy
Was that Battle of Creçy
Where Edward the Black
Made the foeman go back—
Made, with hack, cut and slash,
Of false Frenchmen a hash.

So, Frenchmen, take warning,
No part of it scorning,
For there were slain Frenchmen,
Varlets and henchmen,
Marquises, dukes,
Johns, Marks and Lukes—
So gory and messy
Was that Battle of Creçy!

A SCHOOLBOY OF 12

CAPTAIN EDWARD TEACH (commonly known as BLACKBEARD)
engraving by J. Basire after J. Nicholls, 1734

66

The Coasts of High Barbary

LOOK ahead, look astarn, look the weather and the lee.
Blow high! blow low! and so sail-ed we.
I see a wreck to wind-ward and a lofty ship to lee,
A-sailing down all on the coasts of High Barbary.

O are you a pirate or man-o'-war, cried we?
Blow high! blow low! and so sail-ed we,
O no! I'm not a pirate, but a man-o'-war, cried he,
A-sailing down all on the coasts of High Barbary.

Then back up your topsails and heave your vessel to,
Blow high! blow low! and so sail-ed we.
For we have got some letters to be carried home by you.
A-sailing down all on the coasts of High Barbary.

We'll back up our topsails and heave our vessel to;
Blow high! blow low! and so sail-ed we.
But only in some harbour and along the side of you.
A-sailing down all on the coasts of High Barbary.

For broadside, for broadside, they fought all on the main;
Blow high! blow low! and so sail-ed we.
Until at last the frigate shot the pirate's mast away.
A-sailing down all on the coasts of High Barbary.

For quarters! for quarters! the saucy pirate cried.
Blow high! blow low! and so sail-ed we.
The quarters that we showed them was to sink them in the tide.
A-sailing down all on the coasts of High Barbary.

With cutlass and gun O we fought for hours three;
Blow high! blow low! and so sail-ed we.
The ship it was their coffin, and their grave it was the sea.
A-sailing down all on the coasts of High Barbary.

But O! it was a cruel sight, and griev-ed us full sore,
Blow high! blow low! and so sail-ed we.
To see them all a-drowning as they tried to swim to shore
A-sailing down all on the coasts of High Barbary.

TRADITIONAL

Kemp Owyne

HER mother died when she was young,
   Which gave her cause to make a great moan;
Her father married the warst woman
   That ever lived in Christendom.

She served her with foot and hand,
   In every thing that she could dee,
Till once, in an unlucky time,
   She threw her in ower Craigy's sea.

Says, 'Lie you there, dove Isabel,
   And all my sorrows lie with thee;
Till Kemp Owyne come ower the sea,
   And borrow[1] you with kisses three,
Let all the warld do what they will,
   Oh borrowed shall you never be!'

Her breath grew strang, her hair grew lang,
   And twisted thrice about the tree,
And all the people, far and near,
   Thought that a savage beast was she.

[1] Ransom.

68

These news did come to Kemp Owyne,
    Where he lived, far beyond the sea;
He hasted him to Craigy's sea,
    And on the savage beast look'd he.

Her breath was strang, her hair was lang,
    And twisted was about the tree,
And with a swing she came about:
    'Come to Craigy's sea, and kiss with me.

'Here is a royal belt,' she cried,
    'That I have found in the green sea;
And while your body it is on,
    Drawn shall your blood never be;
But if you touch me, tail or fin,
    I vow my belt your death shall be.'

He steppèd in, gave her a kiss,
    The royal belt he brought him wi';
Her breath was strang, her hair was lang,
    And twisted twice about the tree,
And with a swing she came about:
    'Come to Craigy's sea, and kiss with me.

'Here is a royal ring,' she said,
    'That I have found in the green sea;
And while your finger it is on,
    Drawn shall your blood never be;
But if you touch me, tail or fin,
    I swear my ring your death shall be.'

He steppèd in, gave her a kiss,
    The royal ring he brought him wi';

Her breath was strang, her hair was lang,
   And twisted ance about the tree,
And with a swing she came about:
   'Come to Craigy's sea, and kiss with me.

'Here is a royal brand,'[1] she said,
   'That I have found in the green sea;
And while your body it is on,
   Drawn shall your blood never be;
But if you touch me, tail or fin,
   I swear my brand your death shall be.'

He steppèd in, gave her a kiss,
   The royal brand he brought him wi';
Her breath was sweet, her hair grew short,
   And twisted nane about the tree,
And smilingly she came about,
   As fair a woman as fair could be.

Thomas Rhymer

TRUE Thomas lay o'er yond grassy bank,
   And he beheld a ladie gay,
A ladie that was brisk and bold,
   Come riding o'er the fernie brae.

Her skirt was of the grass-green silk,
   Her mantel of the velvet fine,
At ilka tett[2] of her horse's mane
   Hung fifty silver bells and nine.

---

[1] Sword.   [2] Each lock.

True Thomas he took off his hat,
    And bowed him low down till his knee:
'All hail, thou mighty Queen of Heaven!
    For your peer on earth I never did see.'

'O no, O no, True Thomas,' she says,
    'That name does not belong to me;
I am but the queen of fair Elfland,
    And I'm come here for to visit thee.

'But ye maun go wi' me now, Thomas,
    True Thomas, ye maun go wi' me,
For ye maun serve me seven years,
    Thro' weel or wae, as may chance to be.'

She turned about her milk-white steed,
    And took True Thomas up behind,
And aye whene'er her bridle rang,
    The steed flew swifter than the wind.

For forty days and forty nights
    He wade thro' red blude to the knee,
And he saw neither sun nor moon,
    But heard the roaring of the sea.

O they rade on, and further on,
    Until they came to a garden green:
'Light down, light down, ye ladie free,
    Some of that fruit let me pull to thee.'

'O no, O no, True Thomas,' she says,
    'That fruit maun not be touched by thee,

For a' the plagues that are in hell
   Light on the fruit of this countrie.

'But I have a loaf here in my lap,
   Likewise a bottle of claret wine,
And now ere we go farther on,
   We'll rest a while, and ye may dine.'

When he had eaten and drunk his fill;
   'Lay down your head upon my knee,'
The ladie sayd, 'ere we climb yon hill,
   And I will show you fairlies[1] three.

'O see not ye yon narrow road,
   So thick beset wi' thorns and briers?
That is the path of righteousness,
   Tho' after it but few enquires.

'And see not ye that braid braid road,
   That lies across yon lillie leven?[2]
That is the path of wickedness,
   Tho' some call it the road to heaven.

'And see not ye that bonny road,
   Which winds about the fernie brae?
That is the road to fair Elfland,
   Where you and I this night maun gae.

'But, Thomas, ye maun hold your tongue,
   Whatever you may hear or see,
For gin ae word you should chance to speak,
   You will ne'er get back to your ain countrie.'

[1] Marvels.   [2] Glade.

He has gotten a coat of the even[1] cloth,
  And a pair of shoes of velvet green,
And till seven years were past and gone
  True Thomas on earth was never seen.

[1] Smooth.

Goody Blake and Harry Gill

A True Story

Oh! what's the matter? what's the matter?
What is't that ails young Harry Gill?
That evermore his teeth they chatter,
Chatter, chatter, chatter still.
Of waistcoats Harry has no lack,
Good duffle grey, and flannel fine;
He has a blanket on his back,
And coats enough to smother nine.

In March, December, and in July,
'Tis all the same with Harry Gill;
The neighbours tell, and tell you truly,
His teeth they chatter, chatter still.
At night, at morning, and at noon,
'Tis all the same with Harry Gill;
Beneath the sun, beneath the moon,
His teeth they chatter, chatter still.

Young Harry was a lusty drover,
And who so stout of limb as he?
His cheeks were red as ruddy clover,
His voice was like the voice of three.
Auld Goody Blake was old and poor,
Ill fed she was and thinly clad;
And any man who passed her door,
Might see how poor a hut she had.

All day she spun in her poor dwelling,
And then her three hours' work at night!
Alas! 'twas hardly worth the telling,
It would not pay for candle-light.
—This woman dwelt in Dorsetshire,
Her hut was on a cold hill-side,
And in that country coals are dear,
For they come far by wind and tide.

By the same fire to boil their pottage,
Two poor old dames, as I have known,
Will often live in one small cottage,
But she, poor woman, dwelt alone.

'Twas well enough when summer came,
The long, warm, lightsome summer-day,
Then at her door the *canty*[1] dame
Would sit, as any linnet gay.

But when the ice our streams did fetter,
Oh! then how her old bones would shake!
You would have said, if you had met her,
'Twas a hard time for Goody Blake.
Her evenings then were dull and dead;
Sad case it was, as you may think,
For very cold to go to bed,
And then for cold not sleep a wink.

Oh joy for her! when e'er in winter
The winds at night had made a rout,
And scattered many a lusty splinter,
And many a rotten bough about.
Yet never had she, well or sick,
As every man who knew her says,
A pile before-hand, wood or stick,
Enough to warm her for three days.

Now, when the frost was past enduring,
And made her poor old bones to ache,
Could anything be more alluring,
Than an old hedge to Goody Blake?
And now and then, it must be said,
When her old bones were cold and chill,
She left her fire, or left her bed,
To seek the hedge of Harry Gill.

[1] Cheerful.

WORDSWORTH IN 1804

from a drawing by Henry Edridge

Now Harry he had long suspected
This trespass of old Goody Blake,
And vowed that she should be detected,
And he on her would vengeance take.
And oft from his warm fire he'd go,
And to the fields his road would take,
And there, at night, in frost and snow,
He watched to seize old Goody Blake.

And once; behind a rick of barley,
Thus looking out did Harry stand;
The moon was full and shining clearly,
And crisp with frost the stubble-land.
—He hears a noise—he's all awake—
Again?—on tip-toe down the hill
He softly creeps—'Tis Goody Blake,
She's at the hedge of Harry Gill.

Right glad was he when he beheld her:
Stick after stick did Goody pull,
He stood behind a bush of elder,
Till she had filled her apron full.
When with her load she turned about,
The bye-road back again to take,
He started forward with a shout,
And sprang upon poor Goody Blake.

And fiercely by the arm he took her,
And by the arm he held her fast,
And fiercely by the arm he shook her,
And cried, 'I've caught you then at last!'

Then Goody, who had nothing said,
Her bundle from her lap let fall;
And kneeling on the sticks, she prayed
To God that is the judge of all.

She prayed, her withered hand uprearing,
While Harry held her by the arm—
'God! who art never out of hearing,
O may he never more be warm!'
The cold, cold moon above her head,
Thus on her knees did Goody pray,
Young Harry heard what she had said,
And icy-cold he turned away.

He went complaining all the morrow
That he was cold and very chill:
His face was gloom, his heart was sorrow,
Alas! that day for Harry Gill!
That day he wore a riding-coat,
But not a whit the warmer he:
Another was on Thursday brought,
And ere the Sabbath he had three.

'Twas all in vain, a useless matter,
And blankets were about him pinned:
Yet still his jaws and teeth they clatter,
Like a loose casement in the wind.
And Harry's flesh it fell away;
And all who see him say 'tis plain,
That, live as long as live he may,
He never will be warm again.

No word to any man he utters,
A-bed or up, to young or old;
But ever to himself he mutters,
'Poor Harry Gill is very cold.'
A-bed or up, by night or day;
His teeth they chatter, chatter still.
Now think, ye farmers all, I pray,
Of Goody Blake and Harry Gill.

WILLIAM WORDSWORTH

In Winter, when the Fields are White

In winter, when the fields are white,
I sing this song for your delight—

In spring, when woods are getting green,
I'll try and tell you what I mean.

In summer, when the days are long,
Perhaps you'll understand the song:

In autumn, when the leaves are brown,
Take pen and ink, and write it down.

I sent a message to the fish:
I told them 'This is what I wish.'

The little fishes of the sea,
They sent an answer back to me.

The little fishes' answer was
'We cannot do it, Sir, because——'

I sent to them again to say
'It will be better to obey.'

The fishes answered with a grin,
'Why, what a temper you are in!'

I told them once, I told them twice:
They would not listen to advice.

I took a kettle large and new,
Fit for the deed I had to do.

My heart went hop, my heart went thump;
I filled the kettle at the pump.

Then someone came to me and said
'The little fishes are in bed.'

I said to him, I said it plain,
'Then you must wake them up again.'

I said it very loud and clear;
I went and shouted in his ear.

But he was very stiff and proud;
He said 'You needn't shout so loud!'

And he was very proud and stiff;
He said 'I'd go and wake them, if——'

I took a corkscrew from the shelf:
I went to wake them up myself.

And when I found the door was locked,
I pulled and pushed and kicked and knocked.

And when I found the door was shut,
I tried to turn the handle, but——

LEWIS CARROLL

Will You Walk a Little Faster?

'WILL you walk a little faster?' said a whiting to a snail.
'There's a porpoise close behind us, and he's treading on my tail.
See how eagerly the lobsters and the turtles all advance!
They are waiting on the shingle—will you come and join the
dance?
Will you, won't you, will you, won't you, will you join the
dance?
Will you, won't you, will you, won't you, won't you join the
dance?

'You can really have no notion how delightful it will be,
When they take us up and throw us, with the lobsters, out to sea!'
But the snail replied 'Too far, too far!' and gave a look askance—
Said he thanked the whiting kindly, but he would not join the
dance.
Would not, could not, would not, could not, would not join the
dance.
Would not, could not, would not, could not, could not join the
dance.

'What matters it how far we go?' his scaly friend replied.
'There is another shore, you know, upon the other side.
The further off from England the nearer is to France—
Then turn not pale, beloved snail, but come and join the dance.
Will you, won't you, will you, won't you, will you join the
dance?
Will you, won't you, will you, won't you, won't you join the
dance?'

LEWIS CARROLL

Mr Tom Narrow

A SCANDALOUS man
    Was Mr Tom Narrow,
He pushed his grandmother
    Round in a barrow.
And he called out loud
    As he rang his bell,
'Grannies to sell!
    Old grannies to sell!'

The neighbours said,
    As they passed them by,
'This poor old lady
    We will not buy.
He surely must be
    A mischievous man
To try for to sell
    His own dear Gran.'

'Besides,' said another,
    'If you ask me,
She'd be very small use
    That I can see.'
'You're right,' said a third,
    'And no mistake—
A very poor bargain
    She'd surely make.'

So Mr Tom Narrow
    He scratched his head,
And he sent his grandmother
    Back to bed;
And he rang his bell
    Through all the town
Till he sold his barrow
    For half a crown.

JAMES REEVES

Diddling

THE people of Diddling
Are never more than middling
For they can't abide either cold or heat.
If the weather is damp,
It gives them cramp,
And a touch of frost goes straight to their feet.

A thundery shower
Turns everything sour,
And a dry spell ruins the farmers' crops,
And a south-west wind
Is nobody's friend
For it blows the smoke down the chimney-tops.

Says old Mrs Morley,
'I'm middling poorly,
But thank you, I never was one to complain;
For the cold in my nose
As soon as it goes
I dursn't but say I may get it again.'

Old Grandfather Snell
Has never been well
Since he took to his crutches at seventy-three;
And the elder Miss Lake
Has a travelling ache
Which finds its way down from her neck to her knee.

The people of Diddling
Are never more than middling—
Not one but has headaches or palsy or gout.
But what they fear worst
Is a fine sunny burst,
For then there'll be nothing to grumble about.

JAMES REEVES

Widdicombe Fair

'TOM PEARSE, Tom Pearse, lend me your grey mare,
All along, down along, out along, lee;
For a want for to go to Widdicombe fair,
Wi' Bill Brewer, Jan Stewer, Peter Gurney, Peter Davy,
Dan'l Whiddon, Harry Hawk,
Old Uncle Tom Cobbleigh and all,
Old Uncle Tom Cobbleigh and all.'

'And when shall I see again my grey mare?'
All along, ...
'By Friday soon, or Saturday noon,'
Wi' Bill Brewer, ...

Then Friday came, and Saturday noon,
All along, ...
But Tom Pearse's old mare hath not trotted home,
Wi' Bill Brewer, ...

So Tom Pearse he got up to the top o' the hill,
All along, ...
And he see'd his old mare down a-making her will
Wi' Bill Brewer, ...

So Tom Pearse's old mare, her took sick and her died,
All along, ...
And Tom he sat down on a stone, and he cried
Wi' Bill Brewer, ...

And now that Tom Pearse's old grey mare is dead
All along, ...
They all did agree that she should be buried
Wi' Bill Brewer, ...

But this isn't the end o' this shocking affair,
All along, ...
Nor, though they be dead, of the horrid career
Of Bill Brewer, ...

When the wind whistles cold on the moor of a night,
All along, ...
Tom Pearse's old mare doth appear, gashly white,
Wi' Bill Brewer, ...

And all the long night be heard skirling and groans,
All along, down along, out along, lee;
From Tom Pearse's old mare in her rattling bones,
And from Bill Brewer, Jan Stewer, Peter Gurney, Peter Davy,
    Dan'l Whiddon,
Harry Hawk, Old Uncle Tom Cobbleigh and all,
Old Uncle Tom Cobbleigh and all.

The Yarn of the 'Nancy Bell'

'TWAS on the shores that round our coast
    From Deal to Ramsgate span,
That I found alone on a piece of stone
    An elderly naval man.

His hair was weedy, his beard was long,
    And weedy and long was he,
And I heard this wight on the shore recite,
    In a singular minor key:

'Oh, I am a cook and a captain bold,
    And the mate of the *Nancy* brig,
And a bo'sun tight, and a midshipmite,
    And the crew of the captain's gig.'

And he shook his fists and he tore his hair,
    Till I really felt afraid,
For I couldn't help thinking the man had been drinking,
    And so I simply said:

'Oh, elderly man, it's little I know
  Of the duties of men of the sea,
But I'll eat my hand if I understand
  How you can possibly be

'At once a cook, and a captain bold,
  And the mate of the *Nancy* brig,
And a bo'sun tight, and a midshipmite,
  And the crew of the captain's gig.'

Then he gave a hitch to his trousers, which
  Is a trick all seamen larn,
And having got rid of a thumping quid,
  He spun this painful yarn:

'' Twas in the good ship *Nancy Bell*
  That we sailed to the Indian sea,
And there on a reef we come to grief,
  Which has often occurred to me.

'And pretty nigh all o' the crew was drowned
  (There was seventy-seven o' soul),
And only ten of the *Nancy's* men
  Said 'Here!' to the muster-roll.

There was me and the cook and the captain bold,
  And the mate of the *Nancy* brig,
And the bo'sun tight, and a midshipmite,
  And the crew of the captain's gig.

'For a month we'd neither wittles nor drink,
  Till a-hungry we did feel,
So we drawed a lot, and accordin' shot
  The captain for our meal.

'The next lot fell to the *Nancy's* mate,
    And a delicate dish he made;
Then our appetite with the midshipmite
    We seven survivors stayed.

'And then we murdered the bo'sun tight,
    And he much resembled pig;
Then we wittled free, did the cook and me
    On the crew of the captain's gig.

'Then only the cook and me was left,
    And the delicate question, "Which
Of us two goes to the kettle?" arose
    And we argued it out as sich.

'For I loved that cook as a brother, I did,
    And the cook he worshipped me;
But we'd both be blowed if we'd either be stowed
    In the other chap's hold, you see.

' "I'll be eat if you dines off me," says Tom,
    "Yes, that," said I, "you'll be,"—
"I'm boiled if I die, my friend," quoth I,
    And "Exactly so," quoth he.

'Says he, "Dear James, to murder me
    Were a foolish thing to do,
For don't you see that you can't cook *me*,
    While I can—and will—cook *you*!"

'So he boils the water, and takes the salt
    And the pepper in portions true
(Which he never forgot), and some chopped shalot,
    And some sage and parsley too.

' "Come here," says he, with a proper pride,
　Which his smiling features tell,
" 'Twill soothing be if I let you see,
　How extremely nice you'll smell."

'And he stirred it round and round and round,
　And he sniffed at the foaming froth;
When I ups with his heels, and smothers his squeals
　In the scum of the boiling broth.

'And I eat that cook in a week or less,
　And—as I eating be
The last of his chops, why, I almost drops,
　For a wessel in sight I see!

*　　*　　*

'And I never grin, and I never smile,
　And I never larf nor play,
But I sit and croak, and a single joke
　I have—which is to say:

'Oh, I am a cook and a captain bold,
　And the mate of the *Nancy* brig,
And a bo'sun tight, *and* a midshipmite,
　And the crew of the captain's gig!'

W. S. GILBERT

Limericks

THERE was a Young Lady of Norway
Who casually sat in a doorway;
     When the door squeezed her flat,
     She exclaimed, 'What of that?'
This courageous Young Lady of Norway.

There was an Old Man of West Dumpet,
Who possessed a large Nose like a Trumpet;
     When he blew it aloud,
     It astonished the crowd,
And was heard through the whole of West Dumpet.

There was an Old Man on the Border,
Who lived in the utmost disorder;
     He danced with the Cat,
     And made Tea in his Hat,
Which vexed all the folks on the Border.

There was an Old Man of Apulia,
Whose conduct was very peculiar;
    He fed twenty sons
    Upon nothing but buns,
That whimsical Man of Apulia.

There was an Old Man of Thermopylae,
Who never did anything properly;
    But they said, 'If you choose
    To boil Eggs in your Shoes,
You shall never remain in Thermopylae.'

There was a Young Lady whose Nose
Continually prospers and grows;
    When it grew out of sight,
    She exclaimed in a fright,
'Oh! Farewell to the end of my Nose!'

There was an Old Man of Dumbree,
Who taught little Owls to drink Tea;
 For he said, 'To eat mice
 Is not proper or nice.'
That amiable Man of Dumbree.

There was a Young Lady in Blue,
Who said, 'Is it you? Is it you?'
 When they said, 'Yes, it is'—
 She replied only, 'Whizz!'
That ungracious Young Lady in Blue.

EDWARD LEAR

Original drawings by Edward Lear

Sir Eglamour

SIR EGLAMOUR, that worthy knight,
He took up his sword and he went for to fight:
And as he rode over hill and dale,
All arméd with a coat of mail,
There starts a huge dragon out of her den,
Which had killed I know not how many men.
 Fa, la, lanky-down-dilly.

This dragon had a plaguey hard hide,
Which could the strongest steel abide;
No sword will enter him with cuts,
Which vexed the knight unto his guts;
But when she saw Sir Eglamour——
If you'd but heard how the dragon did roar.
  Fa, la, lanky-down-dilly.

To it they go, and fiercely fight
The whole of a day from morn till night.
With choler great the knight did burn,
He watched the dragon a good turn,
And as a-yawning she did fall,
He thrust his sword in, hilts and all.
  Fa, la, lanky-down-dilly.

The sword it was a right good blade,
As ever Turk or Spaniard made;
The dragon laid her down and roared.
The knight was sorry for his sword,
And, riding thence, said, 'I forsake it,
He that will fetch it, let him take it!'
  Fa, la, lanky-down-dilly.

When all was done, to the ale-house he went,
And presently all of his tuppence was spent.
He was so hot with fighting the dragon
That nought could quench his thirst but a flagon.
So here's to the knight, and as many more
Who are all as brave as Sir Eglamour!
  Fa, la, lanky-down-dilly.

SAMUEL ROWLANDS

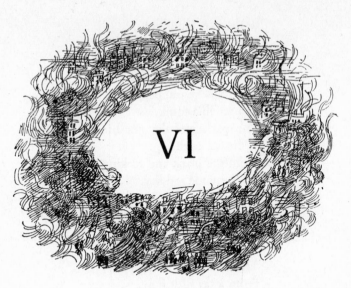

VI

Lines from 'The Firemen's Ball'

'GIVE the engines room,
Give the engines room.'
Louder, faster
The little band-master
Whips up the fluting,
Hurries up the tooting.
He thinks that he stands,
The reins in his hands,
In the fire-chief's place
In the night alarm chase.
The cymbals whang,
The kettledrums bang:—
'Clear the street,
Clear the street,
Clear the street—Boom, boom.

In the evening gloom,
In the evening gloom,
Give the engines room,
Give the engines room,
Lest souls be trapped
In a terrible tomb.'
The sparks and the pine-brands
Whirl on high
From the black and reeking alleys
To the wide red sky.
Hear the hot glass crashing,
Hear the stone steps hissing.
Coal-black streams
Down the gutters pour.
There are cries for help
From a far fifth floor.
For a longer ladder
Hear the fire-chief call.
Listen to the music
Of the firemen's ball.
Listen to the music
Of the firemen's ball.
' 'Tis the
NIGHT
Of doom,'
Say the ding-dong doom-bells.
'NIGHT
Of doom,'
Say the ding-dong doom-bells.
Faster, faster
The red flames come.
'Hum grum,' say the engines,
'Hum grum grum.'

'Buzz, buzz,'
Says the crowd.
'See, see,'
Calls the crowd.
'Look out,'
Yelps the crowd
And the high walls fall:—
Listen to the music
Of the firemen's ball.
Listen to the music
Of the firemen's ball.
' 'Tis the
NIGHT
Of doom,'
Say the ding-dong doom-bells.
NIGHT
Of doom,
Say the ding-dong doom-bells.
Whangaranga, whangaranga,
Whang, whang, whang,
Clang, clang, clangaranga,
Clang, clang, clang.
Clang-a-ranga—
Clang-a-ranga—
Clang-a-ranga—
Clang,
Clang,
Clang.
Listen—to—the—music—
Of the firemen's ball—

VACHEL LINDSAY

Horatius

LARS PORSENA of Clusium
  By the Nine Gods he swore
That the great house of Tarquin
  Should suffer wrong no more.
By the Nine Gods he swore it,
  And named a trysting day,
And bade his messengers ride forth,
East and west and south and north,
  To summon his array.

East and west and south and north
  The messengers ride fast,
And tower and town and cottage
  Have heard the trumpet's blast.
Shame on the false Etruscan
  Who lingers in his home
When Porsena of Clusium
  Is on the march for Rome.

The horsemen and the footmen
   Are pouring in amain
From many a stately market-place,
   From many a fruitful plain;
From many a lonely hamlet,
   Which, hid by beech and pine,
Like an eagle's nest, hangs on the crest
   Of purple Apennine.

And now hath every city
   Sent up her tale of men;
The foot are fourscore thousand,
   The horse are thousands ten:
Before the gates of Sutrium
   Is met the great array.
A proud man was Lars Porsena
   Upon the trysting day.

But by the yellow Tiber
   Was tumult and affright:
From all the spacious champaign
   To Rome men took their flight.
A mile around the city,
   The throng stopped up the ways;
A fearful sight it was to see
   Through two long nights and days.

Now, from the rock Tarpeian,
   Could the wan burghers spy
The line of blazing villages
   Red in the midnight sky.

The Fathers of the City,
   They sat all night and day,
For every hour some horseman came
   With tidings of dismay.

To eastward and to westward
   Have spread the Tuscan bands;
Nor house, nor fence, nor dovecote
   In Crustumerium stands.
Verbenna down to Ostia
   Hath wasted all the plain;
Astur hath stormed Janiculum,
   And the stout guards are slain.

I-wis, in all the Senate,
   There was no heart so bold,
But sore it ached and fast it beat,
   When that ill news was told.
Forthwith uprose the Consul,
   Uprose the Fathers all;
In haste they girded up their gowns,
   And hied them to the wall.

They held a council standing
   Before the River-Gate;
Short time was there, ye well may guess,
   For musing or debate.
Out spake the Consul roundly:
   'The bridge must straight go down;
For, since Janiculum is lost,
   Nought else can save the town.'

Just then a scout came flying,
    All wild with haste and fear:
'To arms! to arms! Sir Consul:
    Lars Porsena is here.'
On the low hills to westward
    The Consul fixed his eye,
And saw the swarthy storm of dust
    Rise fast along the sky.

And nearer fast and nearer
    Doth the red whirlwind come;
And louder still and still more loud,
From underneath that rolling cloud,
Is heard the trumpet's war-note proud,
    The trampling, and the hum.
And plainly and more plainly
    Now through the gloom appears,
Far to left and far to right,
In broken gleams of dark-blue light,
The long array of helmets bright,
    The long array of spears.

Fast by the royal standard,
    O'erlooking all the war,
Lars Porsena of Clusium
    Sat in his ivory car.
By the right wheel rode Mamilius,
    Prince of the Latian name;
And by the left false Sextus,
    That wrought the deed of sham.

But when the face of Sextus
    Was seen among the foes,
A yell that rent the firmament
    From all the town arose.

On the housetops was no woman
　　But spat towards him and hissed,
No child but screamed out curses,
　　And shook its little fist.

But the Consul's brow was sad,
　　And the Consul's speech was low,
And darkly looked he at the wall,
　　And darkly at the foe.
'Their van will be upon us
　　Before the bridge goes down;
And if they once may win the bridge,
　　What hope to save the town?'

Then out spake brave Horatius,
　　The Captain of the Gate:
'To every man upon this earth
　　Death cometh soon or late.
And how can man die better
　　Than facing fearful odds,
For the ashes of his fathers,
　　And the temples of his Gods,

'And for the tender mother
　　Who dandled him to rest,
And for the wife who nurses
　　His baby at her breast,
And for the holy maidens
　　Who feed the eternal flame,
To save them from false Sextus,
　　That wrought the deed of shame?

'Hew down the bridge, Sir Consul,
　　With all the speed ye may;
I, with two more to help me,
　　Will hold the foe in play.
In yon strait path a thousand
　　May well be stopped by three.
Now who will stand on either hand,
　　And keep the bridge with me?'

Then out spake Spurius Lartius;
　　A Ramnian proud was he:
'Lo, I will stand at thy right hand,
　　And keep the bridge with thee.'
And out spake strong Herminius;
　　Of Titian blood was he:
'I will abide on thy left side,
　　And keep the bridge with thee.'

'Horatius,' quoth the Consul,
　　'As thou sayest, so let it be.'
And straight against that great array
　　Forth went the dauntless Three.
For Romans in Rome's quarrel
　　Spared neither land nor gold,
Nor son nor wife, nor limb nor life,
　　In the brave days of old.

Now while the Three were tightening
　　Their harness on their backs,
The Consul was the foremost man
　　To take in hand an axe:

And Fathers mixed with Commons
  Seized hatchet, bar, and crow,
And smote upon the planks above
  And loosed the props below.

Meanwhile the Tuscan army,
  Right glorious to behold,
Came flashing back the noonday light,
Rank behind rank, like surges bright
  Of a broad sea of gold.
Four hundred trumpets sounded
  A peal of warlike glee,
As that great host with measured tread,
And spears advanced, and ensigns spread,
Rolled slowly towards the bridge's head,
  Where stood the dauntless Three.

The Three stood calm and silent,
  And looked upon the foes,
And a great shout of laughter
  From all the vanguard rose:
And forth three chiefs came spurring
  Before that deep array;
To earth they sprang, their swords they drew,
And lifted high their shields, and flew
  To win the narrow way;

Aunus from green Tifernum,
  Lord of the Hill of Vines;
And Seius, whose eight hundred slaves
  Sicken in Ilva's mines;
And Picus, long to Clusium
  Vassal in peace and war,

Who led to fight his Umbrian powers
From that grey crag where, girt with towers,
The fortress of Nequinum lowers
    O'er the pale waves of Nar.

Stout Lartius hurled down Aunus
    Into the stream beneath;
Herminius struck at Seius,
    And clove him to the teeth:
At Picus brave Horatius
    Darted one fiery thrust;
And the proud Umbrian's gilded arms
    Clashed in the bloody dust.

But now no sound of laughter
    Was heard among the foes,
A wild and wrathful clamour
    From all the vanguard rose.
Six spears' lengths from the entrance
    Halted that deep array,
And for a space no man came forth
    To win the narrow way.

But hark! the cry is 'Astur!'
    And lo! the ranks divide;
And the great Lord of Luna
    Comes with his stately stride.
Upon his ample shoulders
    Clangs loud the fourfold shield,
And in his hand he shakes the brand
    Which none but he can wield.

He smiled on those bold Romans
  A smile serene and high;
He eyed the flinching Tuscans,
  And scorn was in his eye.
Quoth he, 'The she-wolf's litter
  Stands savagely at bay:
But will ye dare to follow,
  If Astur clears the way?'

Then, whirling up his broadsword
  With both hands to the height,
He rushed against Horatius,
  And smote with all his might.
With shield and blade Horatius
  Right deftly turned the blow.
The blow, though turned, came yet too nigh;
It missed his helm, but gashed his thigh:
The Tuscans raised a joyful cry
  To see the red blood flow.

He reeled, and on Herminius
  He leaned one breathing-space;
Then, like a wild cat mad with wounds,
  Sprang right at Astur's face.
Through teeth, and skull, and helmet,
  So fierce a thrust he sped,
The good sword stood a hand-breadth out
  Behind the Tuscan's head.

And the great Lord of Luna
  Fell at that deadly stroke,
As falls on Mount Alvernus
  A thunder-smitten oak.

Far o'er the crashing forest
    The giant arms lie spread;
And the pale augurs, muttering low,
    Gaze on the blasted head.

On Astur's throat Horatius
    Right firmly pressed his heel,
And thrice and four times tugged amain,
    Ere he wrenched out the steel.
'And see,' he cried, 'the welcome,
    Fair guests, that waits you here!
What noble Lucumo comes next
    To taste our Roman cheer?'

But at his haughty challenge
    A sullen murmur ran,
Mingled of wrath, and shame, and dread,
    Along that glittering van.
There lacked not men of prowess,
    Nor men of lordly race;
For all Etruria's noblest
    Were round the fatal place.

But all Eturia's noblest
    Felt their hearts sink to see
On the earth the bloody corpses,
    In the path the dauntless Three:
And, from the ghastly entrance,
    Where those bold Romans stood,
All shrank, like boys who unaware,
Ranging the woods to start a hare,
Come to the mouth of the dark lair
Where, growling low, a fierce old bear
    Lies amidst bones and blood.

Was none who would be foremost
  To lead such dire attack:
But those behind cried 'Forward!'
  And those before cried 'Back!'
And backward now and forward
  Wavers the deep array;
And on the tossing sea of steel,
To and fro the standards reel;
And the victorious trumpet-peal
  Dies fitfully away.

But meanwhile axe and lever
  Have manfully been plied;
And now the bridge hangs tottering
  Above the boiling tide.
'Come back, come back, Horatius!'
  Loud cried the Fathers all.
'Back, Lartius! back, Herminius!
  Back, ere the ruin fall!'

Back darted Spurius Lartius;
  Herminius darted back:
And, as they passed, beneath their feet
  They felt the timbers crack.
But when they turned their faces,
  And on the farther shore
Saw brave Horatius stand alone,
  They would have crossed once more.

But with a crash like thunder
  Fell every loosened beam,
And, like a dam, the mighty wreck
  Lay right athwart the stream:

And a long shout of triumph
   Rose from the walls of Rome,
As to the highest turret-tops
   Was splashed the yellow foam.

And, like a horse unbroken
   When first he feels the rein,
The furious river struggled hard,
   And tossed his tawny mane,
And burst the curb, and bounded,
   Rejoicing to be free,
And whirling down, in fierce career,
Battlement, and plank, and pier,
   Rushed headlong to the sea.

Alone stood brave Horatius,
   But constant still in mind;
Thrice thirty thousand foes before,
   And the broad flood behind.
'Down with him!' cried false Sextus,
   With a smile on his pale face.
'Now yield thee,' cried Lars Porsena,
   'Now yield thee to our grace.'

Round turned he, as not deigning
   Those craven ranks to see;
Nought spake he to Lars Porsena,
   To Sextus nought spake he:
But he saw on Palatinus
   The white porch of his home;
And he spake to the noble river
   That rolls by the towers of Rome.

'Oh, Tiber! father Tiber!
    To whom the Romans pray,
A Roman's life, a Roman's arms,
    Take thou in charge this day!'
So he spake, and speaking sheathed
    The good sword by his side,
And with his harness on his back
    Plunged headlong in the tide.

No sound of joy or sorrow
    Was heard from either bank;
But friends and foes in dumb surprise,
With parted lips and straining eyes,
    Stood gazing where he sank;
And when above the surges
    They saw his crest appear,
All Rome sent forth a rapturous cry,
And even the ranks of Tuscany
    Could scarce forbear to cheer.

But fiercely ran the current,
    Swollen high by months of rain:
And fast his blood was flowing;
    And he was sore in pain,
And heavy with his armour,
    And spent with changing blows:
And oft they thought him sinking,
    But still again he rose.

Never, I ween, did swimmer,
    In such an evil case,
Struggle through such a raging flood
    Safe to the landing-place;

But his limbs were borne up bravely
   By the brave heart within,
And our good father Tiber
   Bare bravely up his chin.

'Curse on him!' quoth false Sextus;
   'Will not the villain drown?
But for this stay, ere close of day
   We should have sacked the town!'
'Heaven help him!' quoth Lars Porsena,
   'And bring him safe to shore;
For such a gallant feat of arms
   Was never seen before.'

And now he feels the bottom;
   Now on dry earth he stands,
Now round him throng the Fathers
   To press his gory hands;
And now, with shouts and clapping,
   And noise of weeping loud,
He enters through the River-Gate,
   Borne by the joyous crowd.

And still his name sounds stirring
   Unto the men of Rome,
As the trumpet-blast that cries to them
   To charge the Volscian home;
And wives still pray to Juno
   For boys with hearts as bold
As his who kept the bridge so well
   In the brave days of old.

LORD MACAULAY

INDEX OF TITLES AND FIRST LINES

Titles are given in italic type

116

Windy Day, A 3
Within a churchyard, on a recent grave 20
Within a thick and spreading hawthorn bush 8
Within that porch, across the way 29

Yankee Ship, A 52
Yarn of the 'Nancy Bell', The 89
Ye have been fresh and green 38

INDEX OF AUTHORS